I'M THE KING
OF THE MOUNTAIN

by Joy Cowley
illustrated by Dick Frizzell

LEARNING
MEDIA®

Flea went down the road singing,
"I'm the King of the Mountain.
I'm the King of the Mountain."

2

"Stop!" said Beetle.
"Who's the King of the Mountain?"

Flea shook with fear.
"You are, O Beetle."

So Beetle went down the road singing,
"I'm the King of the Mountain.
I'm the King of the Mountain."

"Stop!" said Lizard.
"Who's the King of the Mountain?"

Beetle shook with fear.
"You are, O Lizard."

So Lizard went down the road singing,
*"I'm the King of the Mountain.
I'm the King of the Mountain."*

"Stop!" said Rooster.
"Who's the King of the Mountain?"

Lizard shook with fear.
"You are, O Rooster."

So Rooster went down the road singing,
"I'm the King of the Mountain.
I'm the King of the Mountain."

"Stop!" said Dog.
"Who's the King of the Mountain?"

Rooster shook with fear.
"You are, O Dog."

So Dog went down the road singing,
"I'm the King of the Mountain.
I'm the King of the Mountain."

"Stop!" said Cow.
"Who's the King of the Mountain?"

Dog shook with fear.
"You are, O Cow."

So Cow went down the road singing,
*"I'm the King of the Mountain.
I'm the King of the Mountain."*

"Stop!" said a voice
in Cow's ear.
Cow stopped.
She looked this way.
She looked that way.

"There is no one here," she cried.
"It must be a ghost!"

"Who's the King of the Mountain?"
said the voice in Cow's ear.

Cow shook with fear.
"You are, O Ghost."

Flea hopped out of Cow's ear.

He hopped over Cow's back,

down Cow's tail,

and onto the ground.

Then Flea went down the road singing,
*"I'm the King of the Mountain.
I'm the King of the Mountain."*

I'm the King of the Moun – tain.

I'm the King of the Moun – tain.